between pianistic brilliance and spare two-part writing. No-one can object to the taking-over of the lower G♯'s by the l.h. in bb.40–1 (or the C♯'s in bb.131–2) if the fact is not apparent to the ear. Practise the abrupt ending by carrying through the l.h. figure into b.188 and then omitting it: any self-conscious gesture will spoil the simple humour of its punctuality.

D.M.

Editorial notes

In the printing of the text a distinction has been made between original and editorial markings. Slurs and ties added editorially are indicated by a small perpendicular stroke; editorial staccato marks (whether dots or wedges), dynamic markings and accidentals are indicated by the use of smaller type.

Editorial realizations of ornaments are shown in small notes above the text at the first occurrence of the ornament concerned in each movement. These realizations are based on the leading sources contemporary with Mozart, such as C. P. E. Bach's *Versuch über das wahre Art das Clavier zu spielen* (1753–62), Leopold Mozart's *Versuch einer gründlichen Violinschule* (1756) and Daniel Gottlob Türk's *Clavierschule* (1789). Our suggestions should not be taken as mandatory; any proper realization must take account of the tempo chosen for the movement concerned and the player's capabilities, and in a trill a player should feel free to play more notes, or fewer, as seems right. No ornament that feels awkward to the player, or sounds clumsy, is being satisfactorily realized. A player who wants to vary the realization of ornaments more extensively, however, would be well advised first to consult the writings of contemporary authorities, or failing that a summary of their views in a good modern reference work; he should note that except in very rare circumstances a trill should begin on the upper note in music of this period.

TEXTUAL NOTES

Composition   Vienna, July 1789 (according to Mozart's catalogue)

Source   first edition, as *Sonate pour le pianoforte composée par W.A. Mozart. Oeuvre posthume* (Vienna: Bureau d'Arts et d'Industrie, 1805) (no.427)

Notes   Mozart's autograph of this sonata does not survive. The first edition appeared on 16 February 1805; a further edition was issued later in the same year by André, in Offenbach.

1st movt
bar
2,3   RH slurs possibly 2, *4–6* and 3, *2–4*; LH small notes not in source but in Mozart's thematic catalogue and André edn (also 100–1)
27   LH *5–6* crotchets
41   LH *5* crotchet
100,101   see 2, 3

2nd movt
1   RH all 1 slur
10   LH apparently slur across *2–7*, but this must be a poorly engraved tie *1–10*; cf. 53, where tie is short but unambiguous
48   LH slur to 49, *1*
49   LH slur covers to end of bar
54   RH slur only to *18*

3rd movt
57   LH *2*: some edns 'correct' *f♯* to *d* (and *b* to *g* in 148), but consistency of source suggests this is what Mozart wanted
96,98   LH slurs *1–4*: cf. 27, 29, 118 – but see also 120
97   RH *4* ?♮; cf. *3* etc.
98   see 96
120   RH slur *1–4*; see 96
148   see 57

Abbreviations in Textual Notes

cf. – *confer* [compare]; dsq – demisemiquaver; edn – edition; K – no. in Köchel catalogue of Mozart's works (no. before / is original no., no. after is that in 6th edn, 1964); LH – left hand; movt – movement; q – quaver; RH – right hand; sq – semiquaver; stacc. – staccato

Pitch – *c'* is middle C, *d'* the note above, *b* the note below; *c''* and *c'''* one and two octaves above, *c, C* and *C'* one, two and three octaves below

Numerals – arabic numerals in roman normally denote bar nos.; arabic in italic denote note nos. within the bar, counting left to right, chords downwards, and including all grace notes as notated

SONATA in D

K 576 (1789)

A. B. 1518

Mozart

Sonata in D

FOR PIANO

K. 576

Edited by STANLEY SADIE

Fingering and performance
notes by DENIS MATTHEWS

The Associated Board of
the Royal Schools of Music

SONATA in D, K576

'So it all depends, my only friend, upon whether you will or can lend me another 500 gulden' (Mozart to Michael Puchberg, 14 July 1789). The irony of Mozart's poverty is revealed in the letters of his last years, but meanwhile two commissions promised to bring in something: six quartets for the King of Prussia, and six piano sonatas for Princess Frederica. Of these, only three quartets and, apparently, one sonata were completed. Mozart later described the quartets (K575, K589, K590) as 'those very difficult works'. Their high-ranging and soloistic cello parts – the King was a cellist – led to some daring experiments in style and texture. It is not surprising that the one sonata was affected, too, in spite of Mozart's comment that the proposed series would be 'light' or 'easy'. K576, the present work, is deceptively hard even for experienced players. Both first and last movements are beset with contrapuntal hurdles hardly to be expected from their innocent-looking opening themes; while the middle section of the slow movement breaks out into a *concertante* dialogue (bb.26–30) that recalls the manner of the 'Prussian' quartets and the Divertimento for string trio, K563. Pianists are advised to study the sonata in relation to these works, and also to the earlier Duos for violin and viola, K423–4. The most teasing passages in the sonata are in fact in only two parts, and they stand or fall on the independence, and dependence, of the hands. These should be borne in mind at the outset: instinct may need tempering with reason, since too fast a tempo can lead to disaster – or at least to the musical disaster of inconsistency. Bar 141 in the first movement and b.101 in the finale are useful touchstones.

This sonata suffers more than most from a casual or careless approach. Players coming to it from the dramatic A minor or C minor sonatas may find it emotionally cool, but those who have studied K570 in B♭ will be prepared for its 'late' manner: economy of notes, a natural turning to counterpoint, and – in sonata-form movements – a tendency to monothematicism. (This awkward but useful word indicates that the second subject begins by developing the first, more common in Haydn than Mozart: the first movement of K570 and the first and last of K576 do just this.) An intellectual delight in canons and invertible counterpoint should not encourage dryness, for Mozart was not the only great composer to rediscover the virtues of J. S. Bach in his maturity.

1 The opening subject, based on the common chord, invited canonic treatment. Notice that the passages at bb.28 & 138 are in canon at a quaver's distance; those beginning at bb.63 & 70 at a bar's and half-a-bar's respectively. From the start, therefore, the quavers should be steady enough to fit in with, and give way to, semiquaver movement: this firmness should be preserved throughout (e.g. the l.h. entry at the end of b.8). Dynamics: the sparsity of original marks throws a greater-than-usual responsibility on to the player, and the traditions of past editions die hard. To read a two-bar alternation of *forte* and *piano* in the first subject can lead to prettiness, and conflicts with the vigorous counterstatement (bb.8–16) where the r.h. passages need carrying through. A better plan is to read the opening as only a moderate

forte, to add extra weight to the contrapuntal version, and to make the first real *piano* in the second half of b.16. In that case bb.24 & 25 will require a crescendo, reaching *forte* in b.26 and sustaining it until the more easy-going passage at b.34 calls for a further lightening. Such suggestions are personal and cannot be incorporated in the text, but they reflect the changing character of the music. Some editions added a slur over the first two notes of the sonata. This is *not* recommended: a vigorous detached upbeat helps to set off the various imitations later. The pedal should be watched in b.57: all six r.h. quavers are melodic, and the illusion of ♩♩♩♪ will ruin the development of this figure in bb.81–96. The changed order of events in the recapitulation, and the extension (and interruption) of the *dolce* theme, should be enjoyed to the full. Players who cannot manage six notes for the trills-plus-turns in the first subject may be content with four demisemiquavers, but if the practice of six makes for a steadier basic tempo, so much the better.

2 Differentiate between *adagio* and *andante*. Having done that, two features of the opening theme will strike the perceptive performer: the writing-out of the turn in the first bar in place of an ornament-sign, which demands close attention to the small note-values (see the Piano Concerto, K595, first solo entry, and the Clarinet Trio, K498); and secondly the minim E in b.2, which progresses through E♯ (b.6) to G♮ (b.14) – in all these cases the pianist should nurse, i.e. listen to, the diminishing sound in order to balance the l.h. chords and ensure continuity of line. The new harmonization in b.13 should be regarded as a shock but not underlined. F♯ minor (b.17) was a rare key for Mozart – those who know the A major Concerto, K488, will not need reminding of the extra meaning of 'rare' – but the turn to D major (b.24) brings an ironic comfort that is denied in the tortuous l.h.-r.h. dialogue that follows. No player should disregard the smiling-through-tears effect when the F♯ minor episode returns, transformed, in the safety of the home-key in the coda (b.59). The simple quaver figure of the last bars, D-G♯, should, needless to say, be phrased with loving care.

3 Remember that the tempo is *allegretto* and that each quaver must be capable of dissolving into triplet semiquavers. The character of the theme can sound flippant, but will not do so if the player knows and loves the childlike arias of Papageno in *The Magic Flute*. The figure in b.5 etc. is a very Papageno-like cliché, and its sharply-dotted rhythm should not be confused with the (later) prevalent triplets. Grasp also the form: a sonata-rondo in which, as in the first movement, development of the opening theme overflows into the second subject (b.26). Therefore make the most of the lyrical quality of the theme at b.50, and make it as legato as possible in spite of fingering difficulties – advanced players will make rapid finger exchanges instinctively to preserve a true legato in the upper part – and do not lose this character in the variant (bb.54–8). The authentic *p* and *f* markings suggest the concerto-like contrast of solo and tutti common in Mozart's rondo-finales. The strongest contrast here is

8

Adagio

13

A.B.1518

Allegretto

Printed in England by Caligraving Limited Thetford Norfolk

A.B.1518

ABRSM
PUBLISHING

The Associated Board of
the Royal Schools of Music
(Publishing) Limited

14 Bedford Square
London WC1B 3JG

ISBN 1-85472-109-7